A Thousand Fra

And, Military Sketches

Emile Gaboriau

(Translator: Laura E. Kendall)

Alpha Editions

This edition published in 2023

ISBN : 9789357948470

Design and Setting By
Alpha Editions
www.alphaedis.com
Email - info@alphaedis.com

Contents

A THOUSAND FRANCS REWARD.

I.

It's a very short time ago, yesterday as it were, that one Sunday afternoon about four o'clock, the whole Quartier du Marais was in an uproar.

Rumor asserted that one of the most respectable merchants in the Hue Boi-de-Sicile had disappeared, and all efforts to find him continued fruitless.

The strange event was discussed in all the shops in the neighborhood; there were groups at the doors of all the fruit-sellers, every moment some terrified housewife arrived, bringing fresh particulars.

The grocer on the corner had the best and latest news, the most reliable, too, for he received his information from the lips of the cook who lived in the house.

"So," said he, "yesterday evening, after dinner, our neighbor, Monsieur Jandidier, went down to his cellar to get a bottle of wine, and was never seen again. He disappeared, vanished, evaporated!"

It occasionally happens that mysterious disappearances are mentioned. The public becomes excited, and prudent people buy sword-canes.

Policemen hear absurd reports, and shrug their shoulders. They know the wrong side of the carefully embroidered canvas. They investigate, and find, instead of artless falsehoods, the truth; instead of romances, sorrowful stories. Yet, up to a certain point, the grocer of the Rue Saint Louis told the truth.

M. Jandidier, manufacturer of imitation jewelry, had not been at home for the last twenty-four hours.

M. Theodore Jandidier was a man fifty-eight years old, very stout and very bald, who had made a large fortune in business. He was supposed to have a considerable income from stocks and bonds, and his business brought him annually, on an average, fifty thousand francs. He was beloved and respected in his neighborhood, and justly so; his honesty was above suspicion, his morality rigid. Married late in life to a penniless relative, he had made her perfectly happy. He had an only daughter, a pretty, graceful girl, named Thérèse, whom he worshiped. She had been engaged to the eldest son of Schmidt the banker—member of the firm Schmidt, Gubenheim & Worb—M. Gustave; but the match was broken off, nobody knew why, for the young people were desperately in love with each other. It was said by Jandidier's acquaintances that Schmidt senior, a perfect skinflint, had demanded a dowry far beyond the merchant's means.

Notified by public rumor, which hourly exaggerated the story, the commissary of police went to the home of the man already called "the victim," to obtain more exact information.

He found Mme. and Mlle. Jandidier in such terrible grief that it was with great difficulty he gleaned the truth. At last he learned the following details:

The day before, Saturday, M. Jandidier had dined with his family as usual, though his appetite was not good, owing, he said, to a violent headache.

After dinner he went to his stores, gave some orders, and then entered his office.

At half past six he came upstairs again, and told his wife he was going to walk.

And he had not been seen since!

After carefully noting these particulars, the commissary requested Mme. Jandidier to let him speak with her alone a few minutes. She made a sign of assent, and Mlle. Thérèse left the room.

"Pardon the question I am about to ask, madame," said the police officer. "Do you know whether your husband—again I beg you to excuse me—had any ties outside of his own family?"

Mme. Jandidier started up; anger dried her tears.

"I have been married twenty-three years, monsieur, and my husband has never returned home later than ten o'clock."

"Was your husband in the habit of going to any club or café, madame?" continued the officer.

"Never; I wouldn't have allowed it."

"Did he usually carry valuables on his person?"

"I don't know; I attended to my housekeeping and didn't trouble myself about business matters."

It was impossible to get anything more from the haughty wife, who was fairly bewildered by sorrow.

Having performed his duty, the commissary thought he ought to give the poor woman a little commonplace consolation.

But on withdrawing, after an examination of the house, he felt very anxious, and began to suspect that a crime had been committed.

That very evening one of the most skillful members of the detective force, Rétiveau, better known in the Rue de Jerusalem under the name of Maitre Magloire, was put on M. Jandidier's track, supplied with an excellent photograph of the merchant.

II.

The very day after M. Jandidier's disappearance, Maitre Magloire appeared at the Palais de justice to report what he had done to the magistrate in charge of the affair.

"Ah! there you are, Monsieur Magloire," said the magistrate; "so you've discovered something?"

"I am on the trail, monsieur."

"Speak."

"To begin with, Monsieur Jandidier did not leave home at half past six o'clock, but precisely seven."

"Precisely?"

"Precisely. I ascertained that from a clock-maker in the Rue Saint Denis, who is sure of it, because while passing his shop, Monsieur Jandidier took out his watch to see if it was exactly like the clock over the door. He held an unlighted cigar in his mouth. Having discovered this last circumstance, I said to myself, 'I have it! He'll light his cigar somewhere.' I reasoned correctly; he went into a retail shop on the Boulevard du Temple, whose mistress knows him very well. The fact was impressed on the woman's memory because he always smoked sou cigars, and this time bought London ones."

"How did he appear?"

"Absent-minded, the shop-keeper told me. It was from her I found out that he often went to the Café Ture. I entered it, and was told that he had been there Saturday evening. He took two small glasses of brandy, and talked with his friends. He seemed dull. 'The gentleman talked all the time about life insurance policies,' the waiter told me. At half past eight o'clock our man left the with one of his friends, a merchant in the neighborhood, Monsieur Blandureau. I instantly went to this gentleman, who informed me that he walked up the boulevard with Monsieur Jandidier, who left him at the corner of the Rue Richelieu, pleading a business engagement. He was not in his usual spirits, and seemed to be assailed by the gloomiest presentiments."

"Very well, so far," murmured the magistrate.

"On leaving Monsieur Blandureau, I went to the Rue Roi-de-Sicile to ascertain from somebody in the house whether Monsieur Jandidier had any customers or friends in the Rue Richelieu, but no one lived there except his tailor. I therefore proceeded hap-hazard to the tailor. He saw our man Saturday. Monsieur Jandidier called on him after nine o'clock to order a pair of trousers. While his measure was being taken, he noticed that one of his vest buttons was nearly off, and asked to have it sewed on. He was obliged to take off his overcoat while the trifling repair was made, and as at the same time he removed the contents of the side pocket, the tailor noticed several hundred-franc bank-bills."

"Ah!" that's a clew, "He had a considerable sum of money with him?"

"Considerable, no; but tolerably large. The tailor estimates it at twelve or fourteen hundred francs."

"Go on," said the magistrate.

"While his vest was being repaired, Monsieur Jandidier complained of sudden indisposition, and sent a little boy for a carriage, saying that he was obliged to go to one of his workmen, who lived a long distance off. Unfortunately, the lad had forgotten the number of the carriage. He only recollected that it had yellow wheels, and was drawn by a large black horse. The vehicle was found. A circular sent to all who kept carriages for hire, put me on the track. I learned this morning that it was No. 6007. The driver, on being questioned, distinctly remembered having been stopped Saturday evening, about nine o'clock, in the Rue Richelieu, by a little boy, and waiting ten minutes in front of the Maison Gouin. The description he gave of his fare exactly suits our man, and he recognized the photograph among five different ones I showed him."

Maitre Magloire stopped. He wanted to enjoy the approval visible in the magistrate's expression.

"Monsieur Jandidier," he continued, "ordered the driver to take him to No. 48 Rue d'Arras-Saint-Victor. In this house lives a workman named Jules Tarot, employed by Monsieur Jandidier."

M. Magloire's way of pronouncing this name was intended to rouse the magistrate's attention, and did so.

"You have suspicions?" he asked.

"Not exactly, but this is the story. Monsieur Jandidier dismissed the carriage at the Rue d'Arras and went to Tarot's about ten o'clock. At eleven the employer and workman came out together. The latter did not return until midnight, and here I lose all trace of my man. Of course I didn't question Tarot, for fear of putting him on his guard."

"Who is this Jules Tarot?"

"A workman in mother-of-pearl, a man who polishes shells on a grindstone to make them perfectly iridescent. He's a skillful fellow, and, assisted by his wife, to whom he has taught his trade, can make nearly a hundred francs a week."

"They are in easy circumstances, then?"

"Oh! no. They are both young, they have no children, they are Parisians. Deuce take it, they enjoy themselves. Monday regularly carries away what the other days bring."

III.

Two hours after Maitre Magloire's report, the police went to search Jules Tarot's house.

At sight of the officers, the workman and his wife turned deadly pale, and were seized with a nervous tremor that could not escape Maitre Magloire's practiced eye, Yet the most thorough investigation failed to detect anything suspicious, and the policemen were about to withdraw, when the detective noticed Tarot's wife glance anxiously at a cage hung in the window.

This was a ray of light. In less than an instant Magloire had unhooked and taken down the cage. Between the boards, at the bottom, twelve hundred-franc bank-bills were found.

This discovery seemed to crush the workman. As to his wife, she began to utter piercing shrieks, protesting that both she and her husband were innocent. They were arrested, conveyed to head-quarters, and questioned by the magistrate. Their answers were precisely the same.

They acknowledged having received a visit from their employer Saturday evening. He seemed so ill that they asked him to take something to drink, but he refused. He had come, he said, to give a large order, and proposed that Tarot should undertake it, employing his own workmen. They replied that they had no means to do so, whereupon their employer answered: "No matter, I'll supply the money." And laid twelve hundred-franc bills on the table.

At eleven o'clock M. Jandidier asked his workman to accompany him; he was going to the Faubourg Saint Antoine. Tarot went as far as the Place de la Bastile, crossing the foot-bridge of Constantine, and walking along the canal.

The magistrate asked both husband and wife the very natural question:

"Why did you hide the money?"

They made the same reply.

Monday morning, hearing of M. Jandidier's disappearance, they were seized with terror. Tarot said to his wife: "If it is known that our employer came here, that I crossed the bridge and followed the edge of the canal with him, I shall be seriously compromised. If this money were found in our possession we should be lost."

The wife then wanted to burn the notes, but Tarot opposed the plan, intending to return them to the family.

This explanation was reasonable and plausible, if not probable, but it was merely an explanation. Tarot and his wife were kept under arrest.

IV.

A week after, the magistrate was still greatly perplexed. Three more examinations had not enabled him to come to any fixed conclusion.

Were Tarot and his wife innocent? Were they simply marvelously clever in maintaining a probable story?

The magistrate knew not what to think, when one morning a strange rumor spread abroad. The Maison Jandidier had failed. A detective sent to make inquiries, brought back the most startling news. M. Jandidier, who people supposed to be so rich, was ruined, utterly ruined, and for three years had kept up his credit by all sorts of expedients. There was not a thousand francs in his house, and his notes due at the end of the month amounted to sixty-seven thousand, five hundred francs.

The cautious merchant gambled in stocks at the Bourse, the virtuous husband was unfaithful.

The magistrate had just heard these particulars, when Maitre Magloire appeared, pale and panting for breath.

"You know, monsieur?" he exclaimed on the threshold. "All!"

"Tarot is innocent."

"I think so; and yet, that visit—how do you explain that visit?"

Magloire shook his head mournfully.

"I'm a fool," said he, "and Lecoq has just proved it. Monsieur Jandidier talked about life insurance policies at the Café Ture. That was the key to the whole matter. Jandidier was insured for 200,000 francs, and the companies, in France, never pay in case of suicide; do you understand?"

V.

Thanks to M. Gustave Schmidt, who will marry Mlle. Thérèse Jandidier next month, the Maison Jandidier did not fail.

Tarot and his wife, on being restored to liberty, were set up in business by the same M. Gustave, and no longer go junketing on Mondays.

But what has become of M. Jandidier? A thousand francs reward for news of him!

MILITARY SKETCHES.

THE CANTINIERE.

She may be young or old, dazzlingly pretty or frightfully ugly; in this case looks make no difference, she is ever and always the same. If there is much that is evil in her composition there is quite as much that is good. She is a woman although—or because—she is a cantinière. This much is certain—she loves the soldier, and is ever ready to do him a service.

It is unnecessary to describe the cantinière in her glory; that is to say, at the head of her regiment on review days, arrayed in fall uniform, her glazed cap perched jauntily over one ear and her little cask on her back. Every one knows her traditional jacket, coquettish short skirt, trousers with scarlet stripes, and her fantastic boots.

It is certainly a pretty sight to see her when the drum beats, leading the way, and keeping time to the step of the soldiers.

But the drum is not always beating, fortunately! glory and noise do not suffice to fill the stomach, so on her return to the quarters, the cantinière lays aside her gorgeous apparel, and resumes her civilian costume, that is, a skirt and drees, and bestows her attention upon the thousand details connected with her establishment.

The cantine is not what the civilian generally supposes; it is at once a restaurant, wine-shop, café, beer-shop, and boarding-house. It is here that the soldier—and sometimes the officer—takes his morning dram; the volunteer spends here a portion of the money sent him by his family; hussars afflicted with a hearty appetite find here a cheap supplement to the mess-room; troopers under arrest can here enjoy a demi-tasse without leaving the quarters, and here all the non-commissioned officers take their meals.

They pay forty-five centimes a day and furnish their bread: in exchange for this amount, they are entitled to two meals a day, each composed of two dishes and a dessert, besides a bowl of soup or porridge in the evening.

The charges are not high, as you see; so cantinières do not accumulate fortunes as rapidly as the restaurant-keepers on the boulevards.

But moderation in price does not prevent the articles from being good, for some cantinières are veritable *cor-dons bleus*, competent to prepare a dish originated by Dr. Véron.

In the generality of cases the cantinière is the wife of a drummer in the infantry, of a trumpeter in the cavalry; her husband is sometimes the fencing-master, or even a common soldier; but his position or rank is not of the slightest importance. In the cantine, the husband is a nonentity. His existence is scarcely recognized; and he is visible only on great occasions, when there is a crowd, or when it is necessary to quell disorder, which is seldom the case.

The husband of the cantinière, when his duties are over for the day, smokes his pipe behind the door, and drinks brandy—or beer if he is a German; almost all the cantinièrea are Alsatians. Their children are sent to the regimental school; some become officers, the majority become excellent trumpeters.

So the cantinière reigns supreme in her domain, which does not prevent her from serving others. She is generally assisted by a young woman, and by a good-natured soldier, who becomes her soldier, her right arm, in consideration of a small salary. If any disorder arises she quells it, putting the offender out-of-doors herself if necessary.

She does not like to give credit; but she is so kind-hearted that she can not bear to see a man suffer, and it is impossible for her to refuse a drop to a really thirsty soldier. Though she censures herself for her weakness, she does not know how to resist an entreaty; but we must admit that she is generally paid, and that she does not lose much by her liberality.

And what woman would not do the same? How could any one refuse to comply with a request of this kind:

"My good Madame Bajot,—I have been in the lock-. up for four days. I have not a penny nor even a morsel of tobacco to put in my pipe. I entreat you to send me six sous' worth of tobacco—and a quart of brandy—for I am very thirsty—through my comrade, and in a little bottle on account of the corporal. By so doing you will save my life, and I will settle your bill next pay-day. Let the tobacco be very dry and of the best quality.

"Be assured of my eternal gratitude,

"Brulard,

"Of the 1st Division, 3d Squadron."

The excellent woman shudders on contemplating the prisoner's privations, and sends him the tobacco and brandy.

Moreover, if a trooper be sick or wounded, though not sufficiently to be sent to the hospital, she nurses him, dresses his wound, and prepares the *tisane*, for which she will never accept any pay.

If the cantinière is ugly, no one thinks of criticising her.

It is her right, and no one even perceives it; but if she is pretty, it is a very different matter. She makes havoc in the regiment, and all the young conscripts are speedily subjugated by her conquering charms.

It is an old trooper's axiom, that the goodness of the wine is in an inverse ratio to the beauty of the cantinière.

She has a little wagon drawn by one or two horses. It is in this equipage that she follows the troops, and appears upon the parade ground, where she dispenses tobacco and liquors to the officers and men in the intervals of rest during the drill.

During a campaign she devotes herself to her regiment. More than once in the thickest of the fight she has been seen going from rank to rank to carry a drop to the soldiers, and braving the canister and grape in order to give a little water to the wounded. She keeps no accounts at such times; she does not sell, she gives.

Several cantinières have been decorated, and the exploits of one of their number have been related throughout Europe. They have formed the plot of a drama which delineates all the characteristics of "the soldier's mother," under the title of "The Vivandière of the Grand Army."

THE BARBER OF THE SQUADRON.

As a general thing, it is upon the cheeks of his brother soldiers that he serves his apprenticeship—a severe apprenticeship for the cheeks! Heaven preserve you from ever falling into his clutches and testing his dexterity. In former years, before entering the service, he was a carpenter, a mechanic, or a stone-cutter;—his good conduct elevated him to the important position of barber, and since that time he has plied in turn the scissors and razor with more zeal than discretion.

This office of barber is one of the most popular in the regiment; and the person who holds it is not a little proud of the honor. First of all, he has a right to exact a small monthly payment from each soldier; he also enjoys perfect freedom after ten o'clock; in short, he is excused from all drudgery, and most of the exercises. And yet his position is no sinecure.

The barber is responsible for the heads of the entire company. If the beards are too long, or the hair transgresses the limits prescribed by ordinance, he is the one upon whom the blame will fall. The regulation is there; he must follow it to the letter, and shave his companions-in-arms as closely as possible, and not unfrequently against their will; for there are troopers who cling to their hair— the natural ornament of man. The military gallant would love to wear long hair, probably so a loving hand could caress his curls; but the regulations are pitiless.

"As soon as the hair can be seized with the hand, it must positively be cut," says the corporal.

All sorts of means are vainly employed by the foppish trooper to preserve his hair. He wets it every day, or pastes it down with the aid of *cosmetique*, then hides it carefully under his cap.

'Wasted efforts! the officers are acquainted with all these tricks; they pull off the caps, rumple up the hair, and then the delinquent and the barber, who is held responsible, are almost sure of two, or even four days in the guard house.

Those sly foxes—the old troopers—do not resort to such hackneyed expedients; they feign some affection of the eyes or ears, and thus obtain from the sergeant-major permission to wear their hair long.

The days of grand reviews are trying ordeals for the barber. In less than two hours he must shave one hundred and fifty or two hundred beards, to say nothing of the hair-cutting.

You should see him then, his sleeves rolled up to the elbow, and armed with a terrible razor which he has not even time to sharpen. The soldiers—I should say, the patients—perhaps martyrs would be still better—lather themselves in advance, and come one after another to take their place in the seat of torture. The work is accomplished in the twinkling of an eye; the most obstinate beards do not resist; hairs that refuse to be cut are torn out; the cheek bleeds a little, but that is nothing. What is a scratch to a French soldier? Moreover, the barber is a conscientious man, and if he occasionally happens to slice off an ear, he always takes the greatest possible pains to restore it to its rightful owner.

The troopers dread the razor, but they jeer at the barber; they call him the butcher, in whispers be it understood—for if he overhears them, it is in his power to avenge himself summarily.

Barbers are the heroes of a host of army legends; there is, first, the story of Barber Plumepate, who belonged to a cavalry regiment.

This barber, who was very skillful in his profession, had an exceedingly vindictive disposition. Very severely punished one day by his captain, he swore vengeance, and openly declared he would kill the man who had so wronged him.

The barber's threats coming to the ears of the captain, he immediately summoned Plumepate.

"You have sworn that you would kill me," he said to him; "that is mere boasting on your part; you would never dare to do it. Wait a moment; I will try you. Prepare your implements and shave me."

The terrible Plumepate was completely disconcerted. He set to work, but he dared not carry out his threats. Never, on the contrary, did he do a neater job.

On another occasion, during a campaign, a barber in one of the regiments of the line was summoned to shave the commander-in-chief. He was badly frightened, and he could but think of the possible consequences should his hand tremble. It did tremble so much that the general's face was covered with blood when the operation was concluded. The unfortunate barber, terrified by what he had done, shook in every limb, and stammered a thousand excuses.

"Hold," said the general; "here is a louis! If your hand had not trembled in shaving your general, you would not be a true trooper."

During a campaign, a barber becomes a soldier like the others, for then both hair and beard are neglected.

"When one finds water in Africa one drinks it; one does not amuse one's self in making soap-suds."

It sometimes happens that the barber of a regiment is a genuine barber, who knows his trade, and who practiced it with honor before he became a soldier. Then there is joy in the squadron; and the troopers flock to be shaved by this artist, who does not mutilate them, and whose well-sharpened razor is scarcely felt. The more foppish, in consideration of a small fee, have their hair dressed and oiled.

The lower officers, not only of the squadron, but of the entire regiment, give him their patronage; he becomes their favorite, their factotum, they treat him affably, almost courteously, and even permit a certain degree of familiarity.

Louis XI. made a prime minister of his barber.

THE VAGUEMESTRE.

He is always busy, very busy, exceedingly busy; that is his specialty. Do not attempt to speak to him, he can not answer you; do not try to stop him, he will march you straight to the guard-house. He does not walk, he runs; he has not an hour to spare, not a moment, not a second.

This morning before the odious reveille had driven the soldiers from their narrow couches he was up and dressed, ready to start.

Should you succeed in questioning him, this will be his response:

"What a life! what a profession! Look, sir, it is not yet nine o'clock, and I have already made thirty trips. I had scarcely time to take my dram this morning, and in my haste I almost choked myself. How do I know I shall have time to swallow my absinthe? Shall I even get my breakfast? That is doubtful. As you see, I invariably reach the cantine an hour after the others. Everything is eaten, there is nothing left, or if there is, it is something no one would eat, and consequently intolerable. Then they bring me an egg. An egg!" (with a bitter laugh), "an egg! for a man who has been running about all the morning. Never adopt my profession, sir; my existence is insupportable—a dog's life! To-morrow, you may rest assured, I shall tender my resignation and take my place in the ranks, like the others. But what am I doing? Here I have lost ten minutes in talking; clear oat, d—n you! I should have had time to drink my absinthe."

It must be admitted that the life of the vaguemestre is not a path of roses.

He is the Mercury of that company of deities known as the staff of a regiment, and like that mythological courier, he must have wings on his feet. He is also the superintendent of the regimental post-office; all letters that come and go pass through his hands; he must know the hours for the arrival and departure of the mails, carry the letters, and go after them. If soldiers receive money through the post, they can not draw it themselves; they carry their order to him, and he draws it and pays it over to them; so I assure you this officer's time is fully occupied. And yet something more than agility is needed, for he must think of everything. The slightest oversight or the least delay might produce serious consequences, for forgetfulness and want of punctuality are severely punished.

In the morning he hastens to the post-office, then to the colonel's house to obtain the order of the day; then he rushes back to the barracks in company with the messenger.

He then hastily sorts the letters, making a separate pile for each squadron; these he gives to the sergeants, who give them to the corporals on duty for the week, who distribute them among the soldiers.

But the hour for the report arrives; he hastens after it; then he starts off again. The report must be submitted to the superior officers. The lieutenant-colonel is waiting for it; the major is waiting for it, so the vaguemestre hurries away. On returning, he must stop to see a captain who has sent for him; besides, the colonel has intrusted him with a letter to be delivered to a lieutenant who lives at the very end of the town. What a nuisance! He rushes to the place, but does not find the lieutenant. The letter is important; the lieutenant must be at the *café*—lieutenants are always at the *café*—at least, when they are not at breakfast. The vaguemestre visits the *café*, no lieutenant; at last, he finds him at his boarding-house and delivers the letter.

He heaves a mighty sigh of relief. Now he can breakfast; he hurries on with all the fleetness of which his tired limbs are capable; hunger lends him wings. He reaches the barracks. Alas! the adjutant-major who has just left the table, stops him in the passage; he has a few suggestions to make—adjutant-majors always have suggestions to make.

At last he breakfasts in turn; he is the last of all. But it is useless to describe the experience of the entire day.

The vaguemestre is gifted with an extraordinary memory. Every week, when he distributes the money received by the soldiers, he knows the exact condition of each man's account; he must know if those who are entitled to money are in disgrace or ill. Every week the sergeant on duty in each squadron must furnish him with a report embodying this information; but it would take too much time to consult these documents. He prefers to remember.

So, Sunday morning the trumpeter sounds the vaguemestre's call, that is to say, executes a sort of flourish that signifies:

"All who have received money-orders through the post must come and find the vaguemestre if they desire what is due them."

This call is so well understood that the soldiers respond promptly, and without hesitation, whereupon colloquies of this kind ensue:

THE VAGUEMESTRE. Private Demanet, you have received twelve francs.

PRIVATE DEMANET. Yes, lieutenant Vaguemestre. Private Demanet, your outfit is not yet paid for; you are credited with only eleven francs, which is a deplorable state of things. You must devote your twelve francs to this purpose.

PRIVATE DEMARET. I entreat you, lieutenant—Vaguemestre. Well, then, here are a hundred sous. I will keep back only seven francs. Make out a receipt. example second.

EXAMPLE SECOND.

VAGUEMESTRE. Private Castagnol, you have received fifty francs.

PRIVATE CASTAGNOL. Yes, lieutenant Vaguemestre. Your parents seem to have more money than they know what to do with.

PRIVATE CASTAGNOL. Lieutenant, my family—Vaguemestre. Ah! I remember, you are a volunteer. Very well, you may go.

PRIVATE CASTAGNOL. But my money?

VAGUEMESTRE. You have eight days in the guard-house to make. Next Sunday, if you are not punished in the meantime, you shall have your money.

PRIVATE OASTAGKOL. But—

VAGUEMESTRE. No remarks.

PRIVATE CASTAGNOL (*turning angrily away*). I shall tell my friends to send bank-notes next time.

The vaguemestre being usually an adjutant, the soldiers address him as lieutenant.

THE ZOUAVE.

Many have talked of the zouave: few know him.

Everybody has seen him lazily squatting at the gates of the Tuileries, like a granite sphinx on the threshold of the Assyrian palaces. He is on guard. He performs his duty with a profoundly melancholy air, smoking his pipe with feverish impatience, or, rather, watching with feverish impatience all the while he is smoking his pipe, some ray of our Parisian sunlight, which seems like moonlight when compared with that fierce African sunshine, which pours down upon the head like molten lead.

A scrap of green or white calico, twisted around a red fez; a blue jacket, trimmed with red or yellow braid, and which leaves the throat entirely bare; full scarlet trousers, cut in the Oriental fashion; white gaiters buttoning above the ankle; this is his costume.

How can one describe the man?

Short, spare, compactly built and muscular, with broad shoulders, square fists, closely shaven head, keen eyes, a mocking smile, and a bold and decided bearing—such is the zouave, the best soldier in the world for bold ventures, skirmishes with outposts, impossible ambuscades, and rapid marches.

Accustomed to the pursuit of the Arab, his constant enemy, the zouave is thoroughly conversant with all the stratagems of desert warfare. He has learned to outwit his savage foes, so he will always surprise the armies of Europe.

"The Arab is very cunning, but the zouave is more cunning still."

He knows how to conceal himself in a little clump of shrubbery, and steal imperceptibly upon the sentinel whom he wishes to capture; he can advance without a sound, remain motionless for hours together, hide behind the slightest irregularity in the ground, crawl, leap, bound, disappear in the undergrowth that surrounds him, follow a track, and shun all the traps that are set for him.

As a sharp-shooter, he has no equal.

If a position is to be taken, he dashes forward, with head down, overturning everything in his passage. It is no longer a man; it is a bullet. Once started on his course, he reaches the goal or dies.

The zouave cordially detests large cities, and regards garrisons with abhorrence.

In garrison life, the discipline becomes too irksome; he must polish his cartridge-box, whiten his shoulder-belt, wash his clothes, mount guard at regular hours, appear at parade—all wearisome enough to the average trooper, but insupportable to the zouave.

The zouave needs the freedom of camp life, the free range of an enemy's country, a *ragoût* improvised under a tent. It matters not if his canteen is only three-quarters full, and if the supply of coffee is running short, so he has but a morsel of no matter what to appease his hunger, he sings, he is gay, he is happy, he is himself.

It is true that when he is not happy, he is equally gay, and sings even more loudly.

The zouave owes his fondness for adventure and his almost nomadic habits to the African war. In constantly pursuing the Arabs through deserts and over mountains, he has formed habits of living very like those of these wandering tribes.

Like the philosopher Bias, the zouave carries all his possessions about with him, which proves, perhaps, that he is something of a philosopher.

But you should see a zouave's knapsack when he is starting on an expedition. It is monstrous; one wonders if he will not sink beneath his burden, and be compelled to cast it aside. He would rather die. Besides, it seems to be the universal belief that he does not feel the weight of it.

Usually, on taking the field, the infantry lighten their load as much as possible; the officers not only permit this, but require it.

It is not so with the zouave. This seems to be the very time that his burden must be heaviest He reduces his effects to the smallest possible compass, rolls them, squeezes them, and then crowds them, and crowds them, until the straps become too short and the distended knapsack threatens to burst.

There is a little of everything in the zouave's load. An enumeration of its contents would sound like the inventory of three distinct establishments;—a drug, a haberdashery, and a grocery store.

He has thread, needles, buttons, soap, wax, tallow, a thimble, a fork, one or two spoons, and several knives, to say nothing of the condiments indispensable in the concoction of a savory *ragoût.*

For the zouave is a gourmand. It is to satisfy his fastidious tastes in this direction that, having no servant at his command, he has made himself the best cook in Europe.

His *ragoûts* might not make his fortune in Paris; but in Africa, in the desert, how many generals have smacked their lips over them!

Any one can make a savory dish of stewed rabbit *with* a rabbit; but to make it *without* a rabbit, that is a difficult task, quite worthy of a zouave.

His fertile imagination never shines as brilliantly as when the larder is empty; then, he employs all his wits; he searches, he invents. On such days, he dines admirably; but how many strange animals are made to turn from their usual path to take the road to the saucepan.

"I do not ask my zouaves for strawberries," said Marshal, then Colonel Canrobert, one frightfully hot day, in the middle of the desert; "but if I really desired some, they are quite capable of discovering them in the sand."

To-day the zouave is the most popular of all our soldiers; his *chachia* threatens to pass down to posterity with the towering bear-skin cap worn by the grenadiers of the First Empire.

It is to the zouave that we owe the words of the celebrated march known as the "Casquette." This is the origin of it:

One night the French camp was surprised by Arabs. A murderous fire so astonished our soldiers, that they almost wavered at first; but Marshal Bugeaud rushed from his tent, and his presence inspiring our troops with their wonted enthusiasm, the enemy was repulsed.

When the conflict was ended, the marshal noticed that every one smiled on looking at him. He raised his hands to his head. In his haste, he had left his tent adorned with the anything but heroic head-gear of the King of Yvetot; in short, a night-cap.

The next day, when the trumpets gave the signal for the troops to resume their march, the zouaves, in memory of that original coifiure, sung in deafening chorus:

"As-tu vu

La casquette

La casquette,

As-tu vu

La casquette,

Du Père Bugeaud?"

Two or three days afterward, the marshal, on giving the order for departure, said to the trumpeters: "Boys, sound *la casquette.*"

So this name still clings to the order. To how many victories it has led, and will lead the zouaves!

Father Bugeaud's *casquette*, by insuring the success of "Duc Job," yielded eighty thousand francs to the Théâtre Français, and sixty thousand francs to M. Léon Laya.

It is a night-cap well worth the having.

THE FANTASSIN, OR FOOT-SOLDIER.

The fantassin, *par excellence*, is a soldier of the regular infantry. The cavalry pretend that the foot-soldier wears spurs on his elbows, but this is only a stale joke perpetrated before the bayonet came into general use.

The regular infantry is really the French army. It has shed its blood upon every battle-field, and has come off victorious again and again. It is the infantry that has carried the standards of France through conquered Europe. It is the regular infantry which, without shoes, provisions, or artillery, swept down from the Alps upon Italy. It is the infantry that fought at the Pyramids, at Eylau and at Moscow. The infantry is the queen of battles; with her one can go in any direction and always maintain one's position.

There is nothing brilliant about the infantry uniform, and yet when seen in masses it produces an excellent effect. It is also the most comfortable and the best adapted to all the needs of a soldier in the field.

At reviews, upon the parade ground, and on the boulevards there are, perhaps, regiments that attract more attention; but such is not the case if it is seen in line of battle. One should see it maneuvering under fire with the same precision as on the Champs de Mars. Each regiment has become a corps, with its officers at its head. A cannon-ball cuts down an entire file. "Close up the ranks!" The ranks are closed; the void is filled without haste, disorder, or confusion.

Nothing could be more beautiful, nothing could be more magnificent than a regiment of the line advancing for a bayonet charge upon the enemy. Search the ranks; examine one by one these soldiers blackened with powder, try to find the foot-soldier you have seen lounging about the shop windows in large cities, with his shako on the back of his head. The lounger of yesterday is the hero of to-day. Now, danger illumines every face; courage, like an aureole, shines resplendent on every brow. All honor to the regulars! upon their banners is written our glorious history!

The foot-soldier in garrison bears no resemblance whatever to the hero of the battle-field. He does not even remember his exploits of yesterday; he little suspects the great deeds he will perform to-morrow should France have need of his devotion and courage.

The foot-soldier in garrison is the best and most inoffensive of men, always trying to make himself useful, ever ready to do a favor. His tastes are simple, and his desires modest; boisterous amusements have no attractions for him, and he rarely indulges in the bottle.

The foot-soldier, like all the members of his profession, is generally in straitened circumstances.

"For in France as in Austria

The soldier is not rich,

Every one knows that."

It is true that one can not indulge in much extravagance on five centimes a day. Fortunately there are ways to increase this meager income. In many regiments, the soldiers are allowed to find occupation in the city, provided, of course, that discipline does not suffer thereby. Those who have a trade devote all their leisure time to it; those who have only their two hands and their good-will—and they are by far the largest number—nevertheless find a way to make themselves useful. In some *bourgeoisie* households they hire a soldier to take care of the garden and scrub the floors.

There is also another source of revenue which, though not the most honorable, is certainly the most in vogue; this is playing a trick on one's family.

The fraud is generally suggested by some old grumbler who is an adept in the art of deception. A mischievously inclined volunteer, who is a good penman, generally writes the letter. Illness is the usual pretext. It is the simplest of all, and seldom fails to produce the desired effect. How can you suppose that parents will refuse to forward a few francs on receiving from their child a letter beginning thus:

"Dear Mother,—The object of this letter is to inform you that I am in the hospital."

The family send money. A letter arrives, inclosing a post-office order. The vaguemestre quickly changes it into shining coin. But alas! this money vanishes like a dream. And how could it be otherwise? So many friends must have a share of this windfall. First, there is the bedfellow, then the inventor of the trick, then the writer, then two or three comrades, fellow-countrymen—then a corporal who has been obliging, and many others. Besides, it is not considered seemly for a trooper to spend his money alone.

A soldier who goes out alone, and who drinks alone, is disgraced in the eyes of his comrades.

When he has finished his daily task at the barracks, polished his weapons, and answered to his name at roll-call, the foot-soldier is at liberty, provided he is not on duty, or on guard, or on the *corveê*, or undergoing punishment, and he can leave the barracks if he chooses. Generally he is eager to improve the opportunity. There must be something of importance to detain him if he does not go out; a letter to write, some little job to do, a pipe of unusual length to color for an officer who is making a collection. But such instances are rare. He loves long walks. If he is stationed in a small town, you can always meet him in the shady paths in the suburbs. He is generally cutting little switches to beat his clothing.

If he is in a large city, he has a variety of amusements. He delights in gazing into the shop-windows; he haunts the promenades and the public gardens; mountebanks always find in him a patient and appreciative patron, ever ready to laugh at their stale jokes. The mountebank and the fantassin have had a mutual understanding for a long time. "Walk in. Walk in, gentlemen and ladies. Admission is ten centimes; two sous. The military only half-price."

But there is no place like Paris for the soldier. Wine is a trifle dear; but how many diversions there are. This is a city! one can stroll about five hours without danger of seeing the same objects. Moreover, Paris contains the Jardin des Plantes, and the Jardin des Plantes is, as every one knows, the soldier's earthly Paradise.

There, he can spend his hours of liberty most delightfully. He visits, in succession, all the cabinets of natural history. He almost splits his sides laughing as he stands before the monkey's palace, watching the pranks of its occupants; he goes into ecstasies over the wild animals, and shudders while contemplating the reptiles. But his favorites are the bear and the elephant. He never leaves the Jardin des Plantes until he has seen Martin climb the tree, and given the elephant a crust of bread, held in reserve in his cap—for want of pantaloon pockets.

But the foot-soldier would be a body without a soul, if he had no countrywoman. The payse, as he styles her, has been created for the fantassin, as the fantassin has been created for the payse. They love and understand each other. He accompanies the payse, who is usually a child's nurse, in her walks; he assists her in watching the children, when he does not prevent her from watching them; on the promenade, the fantassin seats himself near the payse and pours sweet nothings into her ears, while the children play on the gravel-walk. "Honi soit qui mal y pense!"

In spite of the fatigue that results from it, the foot-soldier loves a change of garrison. He goes cheerfully from one end of France to the other, singing as he plods along. Every day, before two o'clock, his legs fail him, which does not prevent him from strolling around to see the curiosities of the neighborhood as soon as he reaches the town where he is to spend the night.

The *billet* troubles the soldier a little. It is like a ticket in a lottery. Some are very good, some are bad. As a general thing, the soldier is cordially received; though the contrary happens sometimes. So far as the fantassin is concerned, he hardly ever abuses the hospitality accorded him. The *billet* is considered very good when the people of the house invite the soldier to share their dinner. It is a saving of time and of money for him. The fantassin is overjoyed, and to repay his entertainers, he tells them his history.

When his term of service expires and he returns to his fireside, the soldier does not presume upon his superiority. He talks freely but not boastingly of his travels and campaigns. He always finds attentive auditors, for we all love and respect the old defenders of France.

Some accuse the fantassin of being too unsophisticated; there are occasions when simplicity of speech is the height of eloquence.

"What were you doing at Solferino?" some one once asked a soldier.

"I?—I was doing like the rest—killing and being killed," he replied modestly.

Sublimely artless speech in which is summed up all the philosophy of war.

THE SOLDIER OF THE LIGHT INFANTRY;

OR, THE CHASSEUR.

He does not walk; he runs; he is truly the soldier of his age—an age of steam. He comes from Vincennes to Paris in thirty-five minutes; it takes a first class *fiacre* just twice as long.

The light infantry has given abundant proofs of courage. It was in Africa, in 1842, that it received the baptism of fire, a glorious baptism.

From the very first the chasseurs inspired the Arabs with unconquerable terror. It is true that everything combines to give them a frightful appearance in battle; their somber costume, their strange evolutions, the shrill sound of their trumpets, make them resemble, seen in the midst of the smoke, a legion of unchained devils.

When the Arabs saw them advancing on the run they took flight.

The chasseurs have a terrible weapon. Their rifles, which are loaded with oblong balls, pierce a board fifty millimeters in thickness at a distance of more than a quarter of a mile; and as all the chasseurs are excellent marksmen, they make frightful havoc in the enemy's ranks.

It is amusing to see the profound astonishment of the Arabs wounded at such a distance. They believe there is some witchcraft about it.

At Sebastopol, the corps of volunteer sharp-shooters was recruited from the ranks of the chasseurs. Creeping along, hiding in the slightest furrow of ground, they generally succeed in approaching within range of the battery, and then woe to its defenders! The cannons were soon reduced to silence.

It is impossible for any one who has not witnessed the maneuvers of the light infantry to have any conception of the marvels resulting from discipline and daily practice.

Their ordinary gait is a rapid walk, their accelerated pace is the speed of a race-horse. At a blast from the trumpet they disperse in every direction, disappearing, kneeling, lying flat on their bellies or on their backs, loading their rifles, aiming and firing in every conceivable posture. Another signal is heard; instantly they are in the ranks, crowded close together, bayonets glittering, ready to charge.

And an impetuous charge by the chasseurs of Vincennes is irresistible. Dense as the mass may be upon which they precipitate themselves, they cut their way through it with their broad saber-bayonets, leaving a bloody trail behind them.

"They are demons!" Prince Mentchikoff exclaimed at Sebastopol.

The chasseurs are very proud of their reputation for swiftness. Once when an order of the day was read to them beginning thus:

"Soldiers: we are about to march upon the enemy."—they cried: "Oh, no, that does not suit us, we wish to run."

When off duty the chasseur preserves his rapid pace, and his ferocious, almost tigerish manner. His hat is always cocked defiantly on one side of his head, and his belt is always inordinately tight.

Quick and supple in every movement, he adores dancing. It is his *forte*, and in it he wins a success that the Parisian fireman alone can dispute with him. Naturally, the belles adore this perfect dancer; but they should not trust him—the chasseur is even more inconstant than that heartless butterfly, the voltigeur.

In Paris he haunts the shades of Vincennes and Saint Maudé. Monday, Thursday, and Sunday he can always be found at the public balls, near the Barrière du Trône, happy if permission to be absent until midnight enables him to remain until the close of the festivities. He invariably finds a brother chasseur who is also absent on leave, and who shares several bottles of sour wine with him.

****

But it would be unjust not to say a word concerning the trumpeter of the chasseurs.

How the chasseur, laden with his knapsack, rations, weapons, ammunition, and accouterments can run without losing his breath completely, it is difficult to comprehend.

But how does the trumpeter, as he runs with the others, find breath to blow his trumpet?

That is something one can not comprehend.

Milton Keynes UK
Ingram Content Group UK Ltd.
UKHW042259170324
439575UK00004B/341